rockschool®

Acoustic Guitar
Grade 4

Performance pieces, technical exercises, supporting tests and in-depth guidance for Rockschool examinations

All accompanying and supporting audio can be downloaded from: *www.rslawards.com/downloads*

Input the following code when prompted: **KCIRSNELOZ**

For more information, turn to page 5

www.rslawards.com

Acknowledgements

Published by Rockschool Ltd. © 2016
Catalogue Number RSK200024
ISBN: 978-1-910975-31-2
3 March 2016 | Errata details can be found at *www.rslawards.com*

SYLLABUS
Syllabus written and devised by Nik Preston and Andy G Jones
Syllabus consultants: Carl Orr and James Betteridge
Arrangements by Andy G Jones, Carl Orr and James Betteridge
Supporting Tests written by Nik Preston and Andy G Jones
Syllabus advisors: Simon Troup and Jamie Humphries

PUBLISHING
Fact Files written by Diego Kovadloff
Music engraving and book layout by Simon Troup and Jennie Troup of Digital Music Art
Proof reading and copy editing by Diego Kovadloff, Carl Orr and Mary Keene
Cover design by Philip Millard
Cover photograph © Jason Kempin/Getty Images

AUDIO
Produced by Nik Preston, Andy G Jones, Carl Orr and James Betteridge
Engineered by Andy G Jones, Carl Orr, James Betteridge, Jonas Persson and Music Sales
Mixed by Ash Preston, Andy G Jones, Carl Orr and James Betteridge
Mastered by Ash Preston and Paul Richardson
Supporting Tests recorded by Andy G Jones
Executive producers: John Simpson and Norton York

MUSICIANS
Andy G Jones, Carl Orr, James Betteridge, Nik Preston, Ian Thomas, Mike Finnigan, Noel McCalla,
Patti Revell, Hannah Vasanth and Jon Tatum

SPONSORSHIP
Andy G Jones endorses Thomastik Infeld strings, Providence cables and pedal switching systems, Free The Tone effects,
JJ Guitars, Ergoplay guitar supports and Wampler Pedals. All nylon strings parts recorded direct with the Yamaha NTX2000.
Carl Orr endorses MI Audio Revelation amps & effects, and Picato strings.
James Betteridge plays Martin guitars and D'addario strings.

DISTRIBUTION
Exclusive Distributors: Music Sales Ltd

CONTACTING ROCKSCHOOL
www.rslawards.com
Telephone: +44 (0)345 460 4747
Email: *info@rslawards.com*

Table of Contents

Introductions & Information

Rockschool Grade Pieces

Technical Exercises

Supporting Tests

Additional Information

Welcome to Rockschool Acoustic Guitar Grade 4

Welcome to **Rockschool's 2016 Acoustic Guitar syllabus**. This syllabus has been designed to equip all aspiring guitarists with a range of stylistically appropriate, industry relevant skills and a thoroughly engaging learning experience.

Utilising an array of well known repertoire and a truly crucial range of supporting tests, the continued progression of any student is assured from Debut through to Grade 8.

The syllabus has been authored to ensure that each student can develop as accompanists, soloists, sight readers and improvisers, whilst enabling both teacher and student to choose the areas that they wish to specialise in.

Rockschool's long standing commitment to raising academic standards, assessing industry-relevant skills and ensuring student engagement is world renowned. The 2016 Acoustic Guitar syllabus has been conceived in order to build upon this success and continue the evolution of the contemporary music world's first awarding body.

When combined with **Rockschool's 2015 Popular Music Theory syllabus**, this syllabus is guaranteed to furnish every candidate with both the practical skills and theoretical understanding necessary to perform at the highest level, across a whole range of contemporary repertoire.

Nik Preston – Head of Product Development and Publishing

Acoustic Guitar Exams

At each grade you have the option of taking one of two different types of examination:

- **Grade Exam**

  (Debut to Grade 5)

  A Grade Exam is a mixture of music performances, technical work and tests. You are required to prepare three pieces (two of which may be Free Choice Pieces) and the contents of the Technical Exercise section. This accounts for 75% of the exam marks. The other 25% consists of: either a Sight Reading or an Improvisation & Interpretation test (10%), two Ear Tests (10%), and finally you will be asked five General Musicianship Questions (5%). The pass mark is 60%.

  (Grades 6–8)

  A Grade Exam is a mixture of music performances, technical work and tests. You are required to prepare three pieces (two of which may be Free Choice Pieces) and the contents of the Technical Exercise section. This accounts for 75% of the exam marks. The other 25% consists of: a Quick Study Piece (10%), two Ear Tests (10%), and finally you will be asked five General Musicianship Questions (5%). The pass mark is 60%.

- **Performance Certificate**

  A Performance Certificate is equivalent to a Grade Exam, but in a Performance Certificate you are required to perform five pieces. A maximum of three of these can be Free Choice Pieces. Each song is marked out of 20 and the pass mark is 60%.

Book Contents

The book is divided into a number of sections:

- **Exam Pieces**

  Each exam piece is preceded by a Fact File detailing information about the original recording, the composer and the artist/s who performed it. There is also a Technical Guidance section at the end of each piece which provides insight from the arrangers as to the harmonic, melodic, rhythmic and technical nuance of each piece.

  Every exam piece is notated for acoustic guitar, but certain pieces feature two 'assessed' parts, meaning the candidate has the choice of which part they wish to perform in the exam. Certain pieces contain 'non-assessed' guitar parts, which are intended for duet/ensemble practice and performance. Likewise, certain pieces include notated vocal melodies in addition to the assessed guitar part. These have been included as reference material and to provide opportunity for duet and ensemble practice and performance. In your exam you must perform your pieces to the backing tracks provided.

- **Technical Exercises**
  There are either three or four types of technical exercise, depending on the grade:
  Group A – scales
  Group B – arpeggios/broken chords
  Group C – chord voicings
  Group D – a choice of stylistic studies. Please note, Group D only exists at Grades 6–8.

- **Supporting Tests**
  You are required to undertake three kinds of unprepared, supporting test:

  1. Sight Reading or an Improvisation & Interpretation test at Debut to Grade 5.
     Please note, these are replaced by mandatory Quick Study Pieces (QSPs) at Grades 6–8.

  2. Ear Tests: Debut to Grade 3 feature Melodic Recall and Chord Recognition.
     Grades 4–8 feature Melodic Recall and Harmonic Recall.

  3. General Musicianship Questions (GMQs), which you will be asked by the examiner at the end of each exam.
     Each book features examples of the types of unprepared tests likely to appear in the exam.
     The examiner will give you a different version in the exam.

- **General Information**
  You will find information on exam procedures, including online examination entry, marking schemes, information on Free Choice Pieces and improvisation requirements for each grade.

Audio
In addition to the Grade book, we have also provided audio in the form of backing tracks (minus assessed guitar part) and examples (including assessed guitar part) for both the pieces and the supporting tests where applicable. This can be downloaded from RSL directly at *www.rslawards.com/downloads*

You will need to input this code when prompted: **KCIRSNELOZ**

The audio files are supplied in MP3 format. Once downloaded you will be able to play them on any compatible device.

You can find further details about Rockschool's Acoustic Guitar syllabus by downloading the syllabus guide from our website: *www.rslawards.com*

All candidates should download and read the accompanying syllabus guide when using this grade book.

Acoustic Guitar Notation Explained

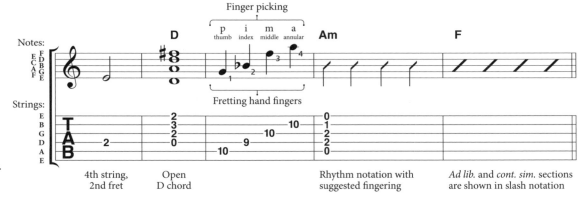

THE MUSICAL STAVE shows pitches and rhythms and is divided by lines into bars. Pitches are named after the first seven letters of the alphabet.

TABLATURE graphically represents the guitar fingerboard. Each horizontal line represents a string, and each number represents a fret.

Finger picking

p i m a
thumb index middle annular

Fretting hand fingers

4th string, 2nd fret

Open D chord

Rhythm notation with suggested fingering

Ad lib. and *cont. sim.* sections are shown in slash notation

Definitions For Special Guitar Notation

HAMMER ON: Pick the lower note, then sound the higher note by fretting it without picking.

PULL OFF: Pick the higher note then sound the lower note by lifting the finger without picking.

SLIDE: Pick the first note, then slide to the next with the same finger.

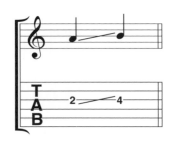

STRING BENDS: Pick the first note then bend (or release the bend) to the pitch indicated in brackets.

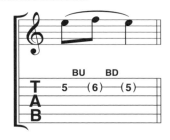

GLISSANDO: A small slide off of a note toward the end of its rhythmic duration. Do not slide 'into' the following note – subsequent notes should be repicked.

VIBRATO: Vibrate the note by bending and releasing the string smoothly and continuously.

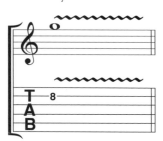

NATURAL HARMONICS: Lightly touch the string above the indicated fret then pick to sound a harmonic.

ARTIFICIAL HARMONICS: Fret the note indicated in the TAB, then (with picking hand) lightly touch the string above fret indicated between staves, and pick to sound the harmonic.

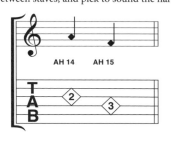

PRE-BENDS: Before picking the note, bend the string from the fret indicated between the staves, to the equivalent pitch indicated in brackets in the TAB

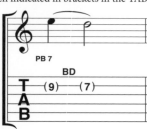

PICK HAND TAP: Strike the indicated note with a finger from the picking hand. Usually followed by a pull off.

FRET HAND TAP: As pick hand tap, but use fretting hand. Usually followed by a pull off or hammer on.

QUARTER TONE BEND: Pick the note indicated and bend the string up by a quarter tone.

TRILL: Rapidly alternate between the two bracketed notes by hammering on and pulling off.

D.%. al Coda

• Go back to the sign (%), then play until the bar marked **To Coda** ⊕ then skip to the section marked ⊕ **Coda**.

D.C. al Fine

• Go back to the beginning of the song and play until the bar marked **Fine** (end).

• Repeat bars between signs.

• When a repeated section has different endings, play the first ending only the first time and the second ending only the second time.

Acoustic Guitar Grade 4

SONG TITLE: NOTHING ELSE MATTERS

ALBUM: THE BLACK ALBUM / 1991

LABEL: ELEKTRA

GENRE: HEAVY METAL

WRITTEN BY: JAMES HETFIELD AND
LARS ULRICH

GUITAR: KIRK HAMMETT AND
JAMES HETFIELD

PRODUCER: BOB ROCK,
JAMES HETFIELD AND
LARS ULRICH

UK CHART PEAK: 6

'Nothing Else Matters' is the third single from Metallica's hugely successful *Metallica*, otherwise known as *The Black Album*. The song is a staple in the band's legendary live shows, usually leading onto Enter Sandman. The lyrics talk about the closeness Hetfield felt for his girlfriend, even when away for long periods. 'Nothing Else Matters' is featured as a playable track on *Guitar Hero: Metallica*.

Metallica are, arguably, heavy metal's biggest band. Their brand of thrash metal and heavy rock is highly acclaimed and hugely popular all over the world. The band formed in 1981 and has released nine albums to date. Metallica were inducted into the Rock and Roll Hall of Fame in 2009.

Their early releases contained many fast tempos and long instrumental passages underpinned by a precise delivery of complex rhythms and syncopation. This approach, as well as their lyrical approach, was changed when producer Bob Rock started working with the band in 1990. Their songs and lyrics became more streamlined and accessible to a wider audience as a result. Metallica also started to explore influences other than metal in their compositions. Their sound remained powerful and direct and their live shows became hugely popular. Metallica are a stadium phenomenon worldwide. They received nine Grammy awards to date.

Nothing Else Matters

Metallica

Arranged by Carl Orr

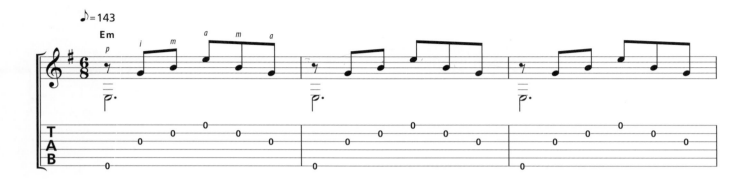

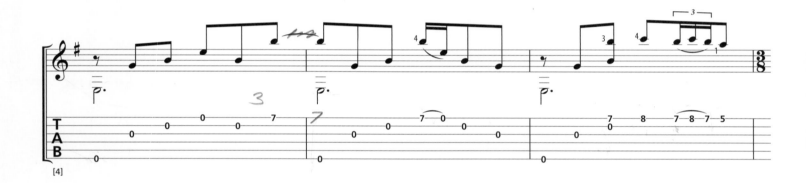

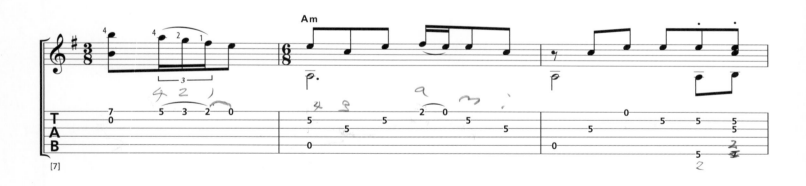

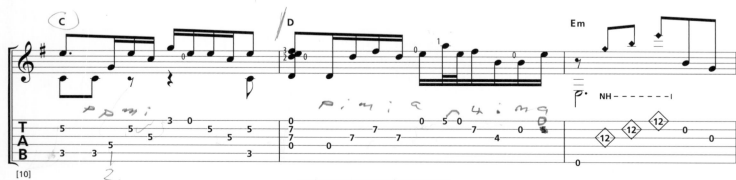

Nothing Else Matters | Technical Guidance

This metal ballad from Metallica makes an interesting guitar study, it bears the hallmarks of a solo guitar piece which was subsequently arranged for a full band.

It is more than a little reminiscent of the famous classical guitar piece 'Romance de Amor'.

The first section starts out with open string, E minor arpeggios, but from bar 5 it becomes more involved, with arpeggio notes intertwined with a simple but highly ornamented melody on the high E string. In addition, there are a few instances where the notes E and B are played as open strings, immediately followed by the same pitch played as a fretted note on an adjacent string, such as the 2nd and 3rd E notes in bar 8, the 1st and 2nd E notes in bar 9, the 3rd and 4th E notes in bar 10, the B notes in bar 11. In bar 12, extra interest is created by the 2nd, 3rd and 4th notes being played as 12th fret natural harmonics.

From bar 25, the arpeggios are more intricate and will require extra work.

As in the intro, assigning one finger per string works for the most part; namely thumb (p) for bass notes and first (i), second (m) and third (a) fingers for G, B and high E strings, respectively.

The solo at bar 42 has been lowered by an octave from the original recorded version, as those high notes simply cannot be reached on most acoustic guitars. There are some tricky position jumps involved, notably from bar 45 to 46.

The ending is a truncated version of the first section.

SONG TITLE: FEARLESS

ALBUM: FEARLESS

LABEL: BIG MACHINE

GENRE: COUNTRY POP

WRITTEN BY: TAYLOR SWIFT

GUITAR: KENNY GREENBERG AND GRANT MICKELSON

PRODUCER: NATHAN CHAPMAN AND TAYLOR SWIFT

UK CHART PEAK: 1 (ALBUM)

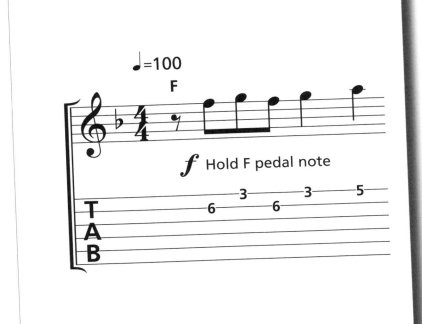

'Fearless' is featured on Taylor Swift's record of the same title, released in 2009. *Fearless* was an international success, selling approximately nine million copies worldwide. Taylor Swift was 20 at the time of its release. *Fearless* is the most awarded record in the history of country music. Swift wrote most of it whilst on the road supporting country artists as she promoted her debut album.

Taylor Swift had a publishing contract prior to her debut album and composed over 250 songs including many in collaboration. She refused to hand in much of her work to the publishers in the hope that she was going to perform the songs herself. Things turned out as she wished and she now has a significant catalogue available to her.

Her style is influenced by Sheryl Crow and Brad Paisley amongst other country artists.

Swift is also a record producer and arranger and is involved in the development of her record's artwork and packaging.

Fearless

Taylor Swift

Arranged by Carl Orr

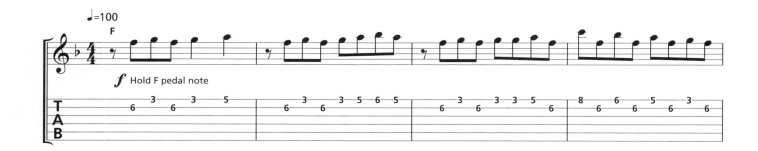

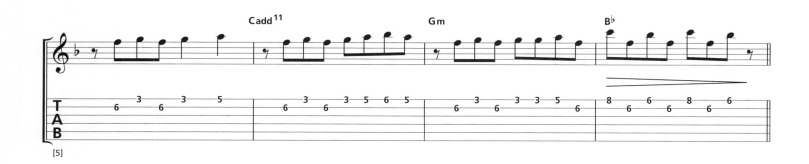

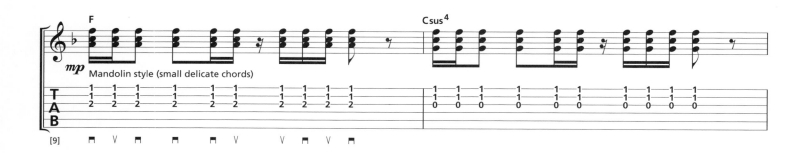

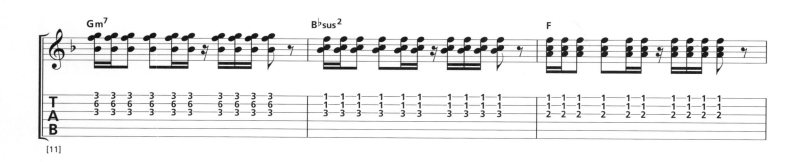

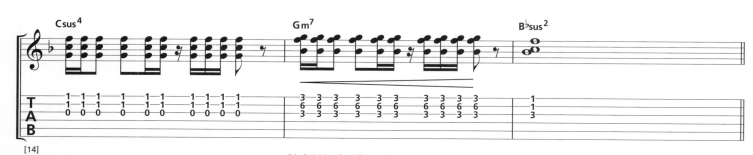

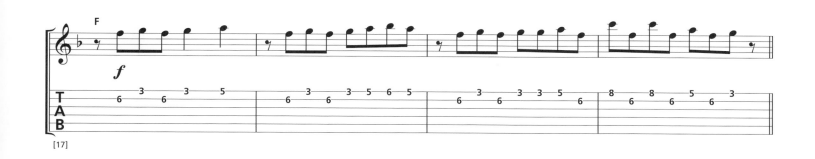

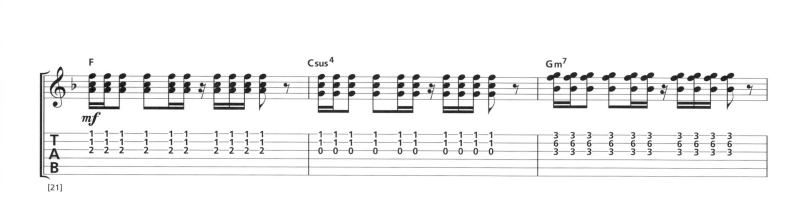

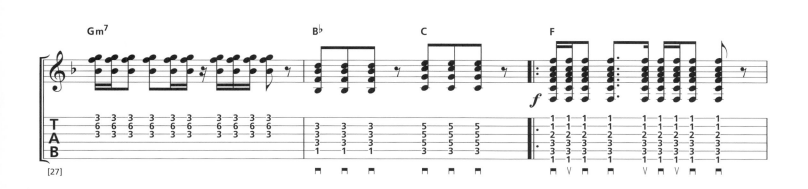

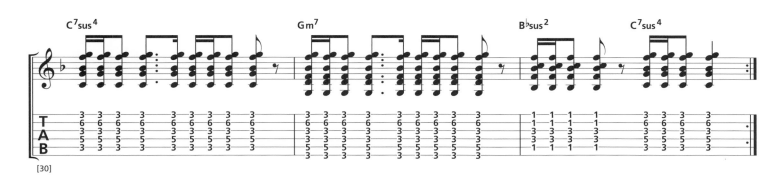

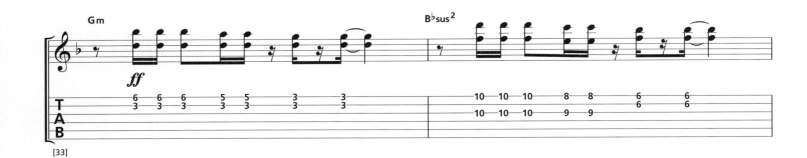

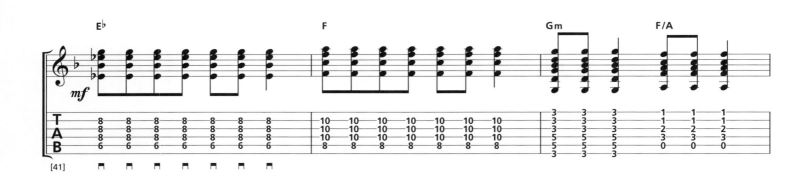

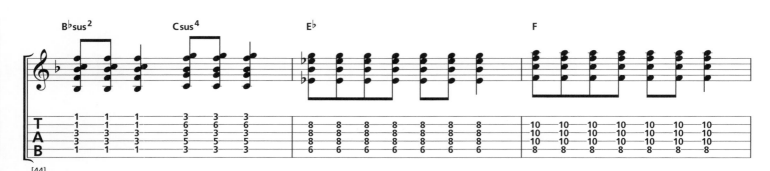

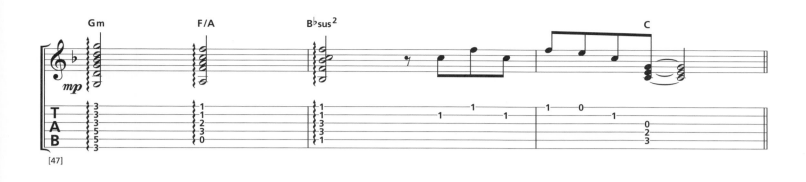

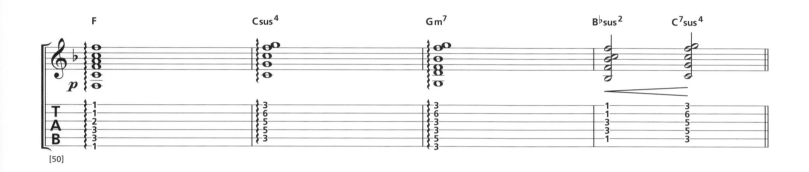

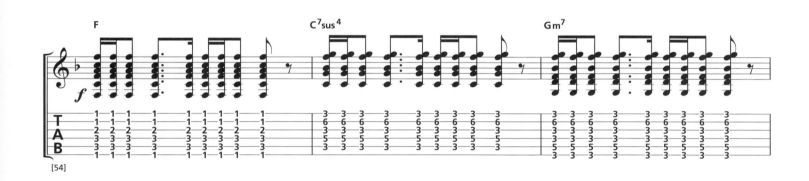

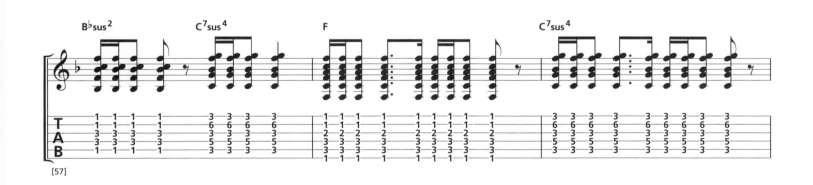

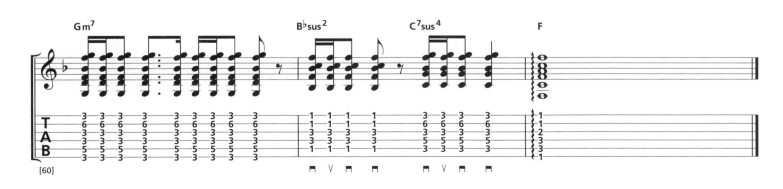

Fearless | Technical Guidance

In 'Fearless', the acoustic guitar is a constant presence, propelling the song from start to finish. The arrangement opens with a simple, country tinged intro featuring an F pedal tone running through it and setting the mood. The F note on the guitar (first fret of the high E string) persistently rings through, creating a feeling of urgency and continuity from one chord to the next.

In the original recording, the chords of the first two verses are played by mandolin and guitar, so in this arrangement the sound of the mandolin strumming is approximated by voicing the chords on the top three strings only, creating a delicate, but propulsive effect. The rhythmic pulse is moderately fast semi quavers, so it is advisable to use a soft plectrum and to strum constant semiquavers, striking only the indicated rhythms. This will give a strong flow to the groove.

There are some interesting chords such as $Csus^4$ and $B\flat sus^2$ which give the song an earthy, Southern flavour and enhanced emotional impact. The first section's harmony is simple, moving from F (I/tonic) to $Csus^4$ (V/dominant), Gm^7 (IIm/supertonic) and $B\flat sus^2$ (IV/subdominant). The solo (bar 33–40) shifts the harmony and starts on Gm (IIm) moving to $B\flat$ (IV) and C (V). After the solo there is a bridge (bar 41) that starts with an Eb chord ($\flat$VII/subtonic) resolving to the tonic and moving attractively up the scale to G minor, F/A, $B\flat sus^2$ and $Csus^4$.

The second section (bars 29–32/54–62) uses similar chords to the first, but with big, bold 5- and 6-string voicings.
As the original solo is on electric guitar and involves some bends that are impossible on acoustic guitar, the featured solo is an acoustic country/rock solo, using simple melodic devices and a few piano influenced double stops that add grit.
The bridge involves a change of gear to simple down stroke quavers for the strumming hand.
The song finishes by reprising the second section.

Joni Mitchell | Big Yellow Taxi

SONG TITLE: BIG YELLOW TAXI
ALBUM: LADIES OF CANYON / 1970
LABEL: REPRISE
GENRE: FOLK / POP
WRITTEN BY: JONI MITCHELL
GUITAR: JONI MITCHELL
PRODUCER: JONI MITCHELL
UK CHART PEAK: 11

'Big Yellow Taxi' is featured on Joni Mitchell's *Ladies Of The Canyon*, released in 1970.

The song's lyrics express Mitchell's environmental and political concerns of the time. It was written during Mitchell's first trip to Hawaii – from her hotel room she could see green mountains in the distance with an enormous parking lot below. She described it as a "blight on paradise".

Joni Mitchell was born in 1943 in Alberta, Canada. Her work is highly respected across generations and genres. Her beginnings were in folk in the 60's but moved onto jazz, pop and electronica in later decades. She is one of the most prominent musicians from the Laurel Canyon scene. Her lyrics address social, environmental, and personal issues from a highly original and poetic perspective.

She produced most of her own work and is a highly accomplished vocalist, guitarist and pianist. Her contralto vocals and her distinctive open tunings on guitar are the vehicle for an original and confessional compositional style. She was awarded a Grammy Lifetime Achievement Award. Her work has enormous influence to this day.

Joni Mitchell is an accomplished painter. She is equally committed to painting as she is to music and has occasionally described herself as a 'painter derailed by circumstance'.

Big Yellow Taxi

Joni Mitchell

Arranged by Carl Orr

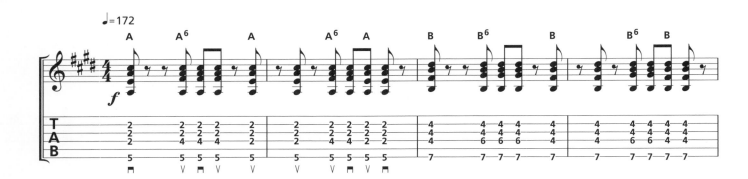

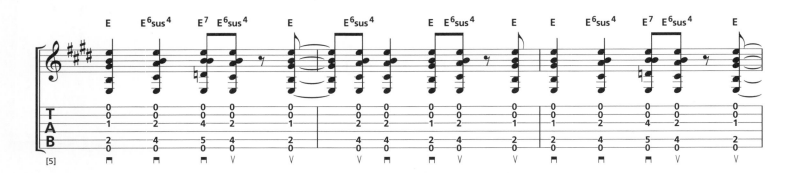

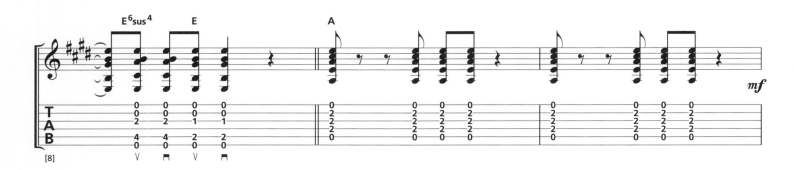

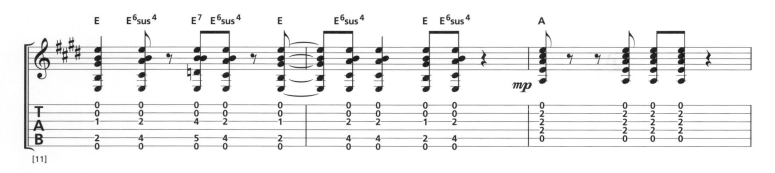

To Coda ⊕

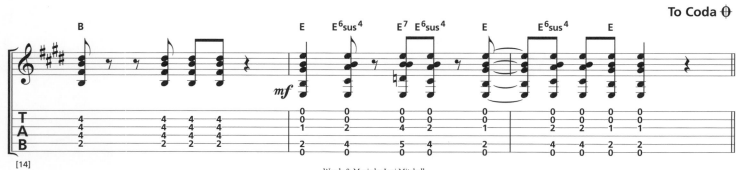

Words & Music by Joni Mitchell
© Copyright 1970 (Renewed) Crazy Crow Music, USA.
Sony/ATV Music Publishing.
All Rights Reserved. International Copyright Secured.

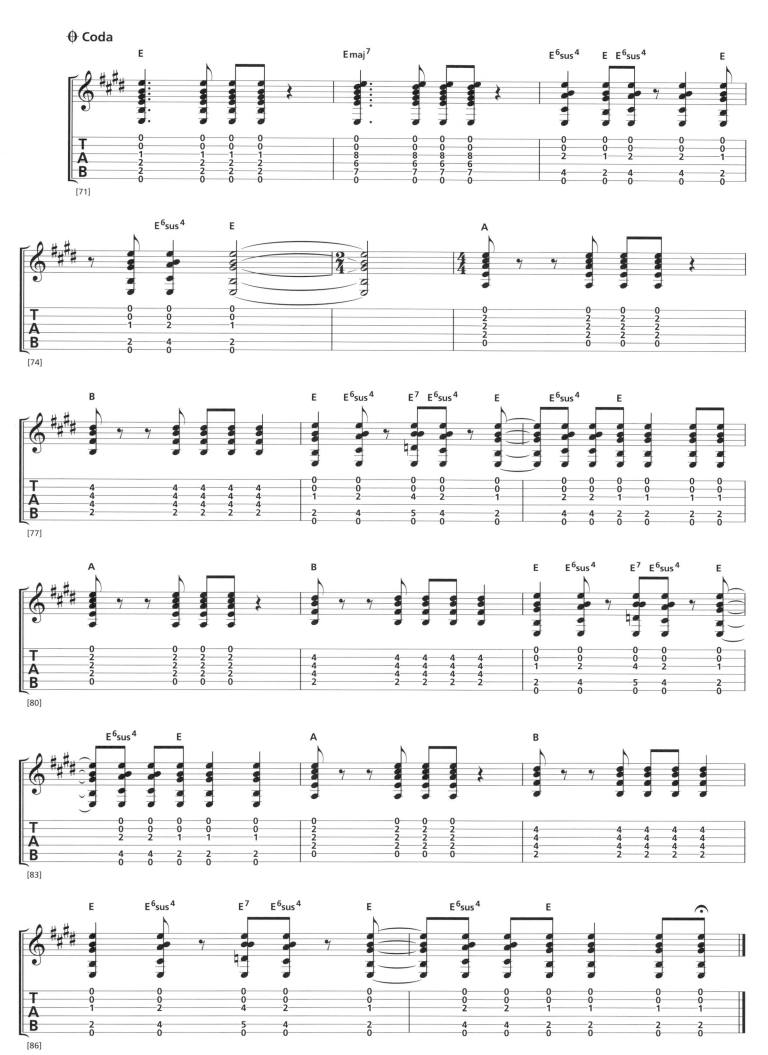

Big Yellow Taxi | Technical Guidance

This Woodstock era classic is one of the most memorable songs of the time and features the very minimal instrumentation of Joni Mitchell's voice and guitar accompanied by a percussionist. The song is propelled along by Joni Mitchell's relaxed yet authoritative strummed acoustic guitar, featuring simple but distinctively voiced chords.

In the intro, after the first four bars of A major, B major and the E^7 riff that recurs throughout is played for the first time; it is a gospel type call and response phrase, always occurring in the gaps between her vocal lines.

The first time through the form should be strummed with a gentle, loping groove. Listening to the original would help emulate Joni Mitchell's unique feel.

From bar 27 of this arrangement, the second time through the form, a Chet Atkins style simple chord melody is introduced. This should be played with fingers. Developing a technique of tucking the plectrum between the first and second fingers will enable playing finger style without putting the plectrum down. It is also playable with pick and fingers. It is important to experiment with both techniques to find out what works best. In this section, open strings are used when possible to allow the guitar to resonate, creating an interesting contrast between the stopped and open strings.

From bar 45 to 52 there is a chord/melody interlude leading into the guitar solo, which can be improvised or developed and memorised. That is left up to each candidate.

The rest of the arrangement is a repetition of the previous material.

Alison Krauss | Baby, Now That I've Found You

SONG TITLE: BABY, NOW THAT I'VE
               FOUND YOU:
ALBUM: NOW THAT I'VE FOUND YOU:
               A COLLECTION / 1995
LABEL: ROUNDER
GENRE: BLUEGRASS / COUNTRY
WRITTEN BY: TONY MACAULAY AND
               JOHN MCLEOD
GUITAR: RON BLOCK, RUSS BARENBURG,
               MIKE MARSHALL, SCOTT NYGAARD
               AND TIM STANFORD.
PRODUCER: ALISON KRAUSS AND UNION
               STATION
UK CHART PEAK: N/A

'Baby Now That I've Found You' is the title track of Alison Krauss' 1995 album. It is a compilation that gathered songs from Krauss' early releases. The song was awarded a Grammy for Best Female Country Vocal Performance. It was written by Tony Macaulay and John MacLeod and has been covered by many artists.

Alison Krauss has a had a remarkable career, spanning 25 years, although she is only 39.

Her songs are introspective and highly crafted. She blends tradition and topical themes very effectively. She has an experimental approach to writing and recording and her view is that what she sings needs to touch a deep emotional chord, whether written by herself or not. She works with renowned band Union Station, with whom she delivers and austere yet poignant sound, supported by exceptional musicianship.

Alison Krauss has received 26 Grammy awards.

Baby, Now That I've Found You

Alison Krauss

Arranged by Andy G Jones

that you were some-one   I   could-n't for - get.   I say right_____ and I bide my   time..

Spent   my   life   loo-king   for   that   some - bo-dy

to make me feel   like   you.

Now you tell me that you

want   to   leave__ me

but dar-lin' I   just   can't__ let_____ you._____

To Coda ⊕

[45]

[49]

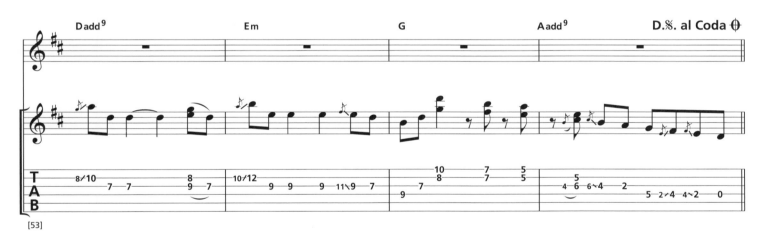

[53]

⊕ Coda

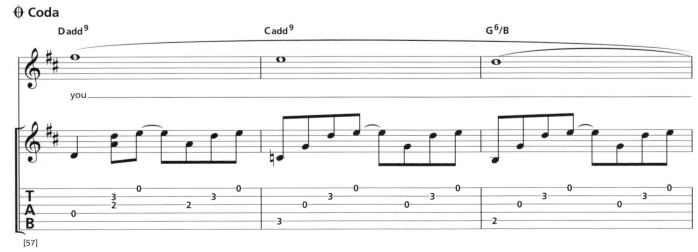

[57]

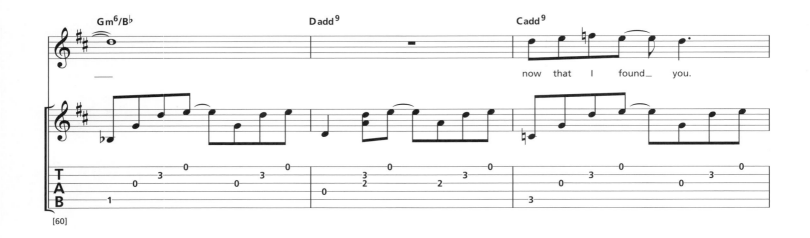

[60]

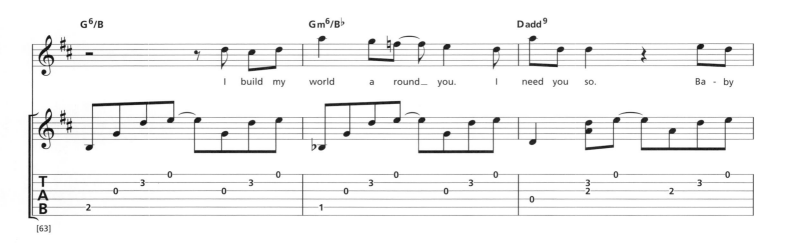

[63]

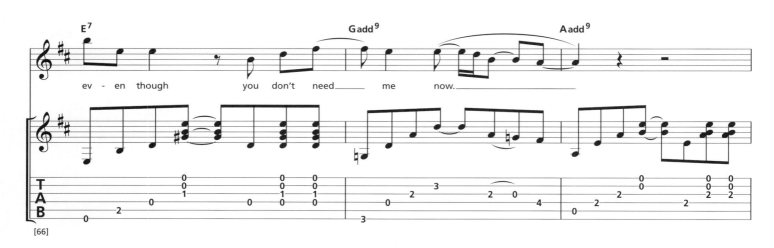

[66]

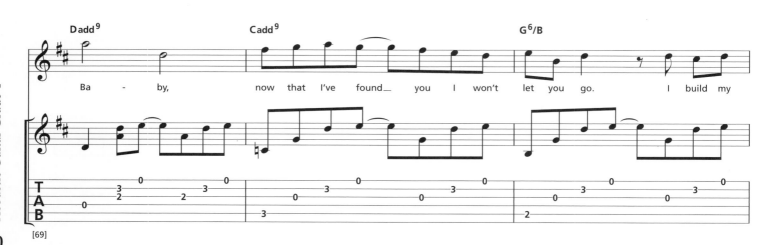

[69]

Baby, Now That I've Found You | Technical Guidance

Krauss is steeped in country music and bluegrass and this informs everything she does. There is plenty of subtlety in the band's approach. Note the use of the added 9th degree on many of the chords – notably the D and C major chords. Note also the G^6/B chord on bar 11. This is quite a complex chord for a pop song but it is followed by an even more unusual chord, Gm^6/B♭ on bar 12. This chord could also be called B♭$^{6\sharp11}$.

The guitar solo from the record is firmly based on the melody and is included in this arrangement. There are some great bluegrass based inflections in it. See bars 52–56 for some lovely double stop ideas. The last bar of the solo (bar 36) is an iconic lick which can be used in other contexts. The first move is a hammer-on from the 2nd to the 3rd degree. The last three notes of the bar are interesting as they bring to light a classic technique in this kind of music. The 3rd (F♯) is slurred into, and back down to the 2nd degree, then moving onto the root. This last note, D, would normally sound unpleasant over the A major chord, but this lick is strongly based on the D major tonality. It sounds like a blues lick in D and this use of a D blues idea over the V chord (A major) works because of the strong sense of key. Even though we are playing over A major, we are anticipating the return to the tonic. Although this works in this context, it is important to let your ears judge whether it works in others. The solo could be played either fingerstyle of with a pick.

Alison Krauss' recording is in E♭ major but for ease of performance it has been transposed to D major in this arrangement.

SONG TITLE: LAYLA
ALBUM: LAYLA AND OTHER
ASSORTED LOVE SONGS /
1970
LABEL: ATCO / POLYDOR
GENRE: HARD ROCK / BLUES
WRITTEN BY: ERIC CLAPTON AND
JIM GORDON
GUITAR: ERIC CLAPTON
DUANE ALLMAN
PRODUCER: TOM DOWD AND
DEREK AND THE DOMINOS
UK CHART PEAK: 4

[1]

'Layla' was the 13th track from Derek and the Dominos' *Layla and Other Assorted Love Stories*. The original version contains contrasting movements written separately by Clapton and Gordon. The song did not have much success upon its release in 1970 but in later years it became a rock classic and its main riff a seminal rock motif. 'Layla' was successful in its 1972 release and in 1992 as part of Clapton's *MTV Unplugged* album.

'Layla' is based on a Persian love story that Clapton read and was profoundly moved by, but its added qualities are perhaps related to Clapton's unrequited love for model Patti Boyd, who was married to George Harrison at the time. They eventually married in 1977.

Eric Clapton is regarded as a true rock and blues icon. He was born in 1945 in Ripley, Surrey. He was a member of many seminal English groups such as the Yardbirds, John Mayall and Bluesbreakers, Cream and Blind Faith. Since the 1970's he has been hugely successful as a solo artist. He is the recipient of 18 Grammy awards and the only three times inductee to the Rock and Roll Hall of Fame. Clapton started playing in his early teens and by age 16 his playing was advanced. He is acknowledged as influential by a plethora of guitarists worldwide. He has released 24 solo albums and has toured extensively.

Clapton assembled his famous 'Blackie' Fender Stratocaster out of three guitars in 1970. In 1988, Fender introduced the Eric Clapton Stratocaster. At the time, it was one of two artist models available. He has appeared on many records as guest, and in movies such as Tommy as well as adverts by Mercedes Benz and T-Mobile.

Layla

Arranged by Andy G Jones

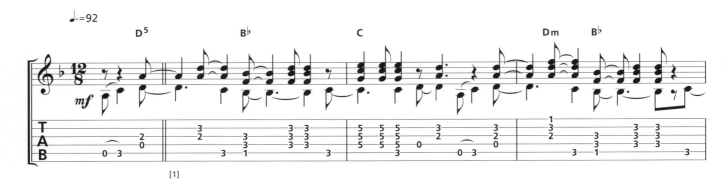

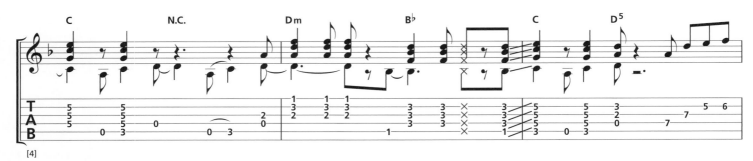

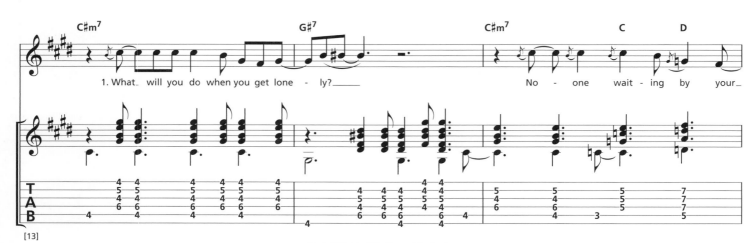

1. What will you do when you get lone - ly?____ No - one wait-ing by your____

Layla | Technical Guidance

This version of Layla is taken from the Clapton *MTV Unplugged* album which presents a radically different arrangement, musical style and instrumentation to the Derek And The Dominos version; it is much less urgent and almost jazzy. Note the anticipation of the chords in the opening riff. This is possibly more fitting to the acoustic context. Clapton still brings some of his blues magic to bear, this time on acoustic guitar.

Harmonically the change from the D minor groove to C♯ minor is extremely bold and is one of many elements that makes this song so memorable.

Clapton starts the guitar solo with a nice A and F double stop idea but bends the F a quarter tone sharp. This is a staple of many blues guitarists. This lick sounds a little like a train whistle. Most of the solo is based on D minor pentatonic. Nevertheless Clapton's phrasing bring this much used scale to life here by adding the 9th to it. Jimi Hendrix also used this approach and it is a defining feature of his solo on 'All Along The watchtower'. Clapton uses the Pentatonic minor over most of the chords in the sequence, including B♭ major. The 9th of D minor (E) becomes the ♯11 of the B♭ major chord. This is pretty bold but Clapton's exceptional delivery effortlessly blends it into the solo. His highly individual approach is used to embellish basic blues ideas. The rhythm of the last phrase is fairly complicated but it is notated as 'rubato', meaning the time can be moved up or down according to the soloist's preference. As the groove stops there is room for this approach.

Mumford and Sons | Little Lion Man

SONG TITLE: LITTLE LION MAN
ALBUM: SIGH NO MORE
LABEL: ISLAND / GLASSNOTE
GENRE: INDIE FOLK
WRITTEN BY: MARCUS MUMFORD
GUITAR: MARCUS MUMFORD
PRODUCER: MARKUS DRAVS
UK CHART PEAK: 24

'Little Lion Man' is featured on Mumford and Sons' debut album *Sigh No More*.

The lyrics are based on a personal story, written by Marcus Mumford about a situation he wasn't very happy with or proud of. The song is quite hard hitting in relation to the band's typical material. 'Little Lion Man' was sampled by One Direction in their single 'Story of My Life'. After being performed at the Grammys the song re-entered the Billboard Hot 100. It has sold over 2 and 1/4 million digital copies.

Mumford and Sons' sound can be described as Nu-Folk. It features an ever present blend of loud and quiet dynamics and it appeals to folk and pop fans either side of the Atlantic, who have received the band with open arms since *Sigh No More* was released in 2009. Mumford and Sons formed in London in 2007.

Little Lion Man

Mumford and Sons

Arranged by Carl Orr

mf - mezzo forte
mp - mezzo piano

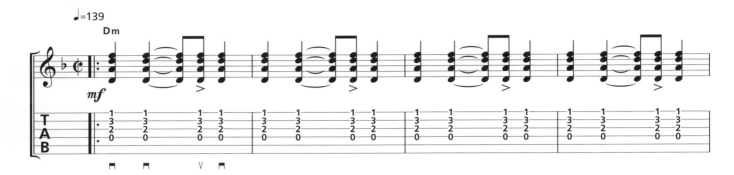

[5]

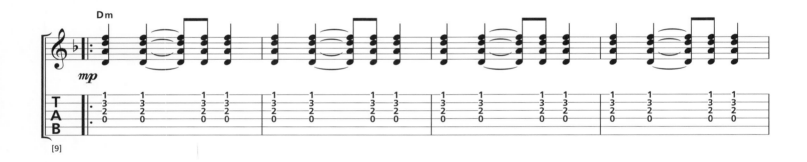

[9]

[13]

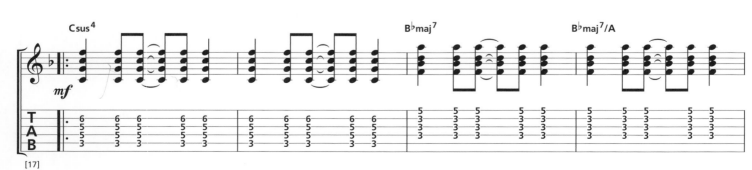

[17]

Acoustic Guitar Grade 4

[72]

[76]

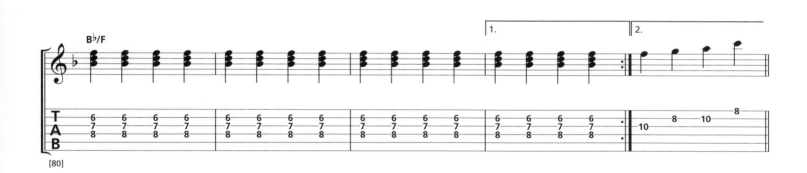

[80]

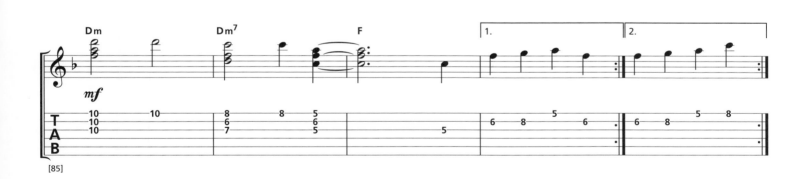

[85]

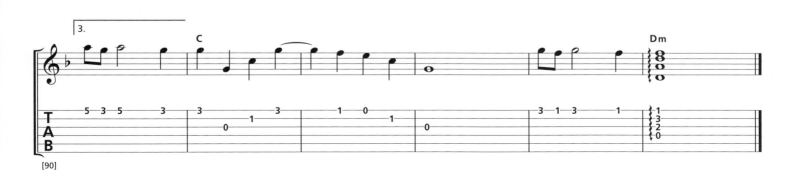

[90]

Little Lion Man | Technical Guidance

'Little Lion Man' revolves around the tension between the submediant (VI) and the tonic (I) chords, D minor and F major respectively. As it starts on the D minor chord, the song feels in the key of D minor, but then it keeps resolving back to F major, with the occasional passing chords of C major and B♭ major in between. In the bridge (bars 17–24) the song temporarily settles on the F major tonality, but then the push and pull between D minor and F major starts again, giving the song an unsettled air, as expressed in the self-criticism of the charged lyrics in the chorus.

This rollicking, uptempo song is forcefully driven along by the strummed acoustic guitar from start to finish. There is a simple strumming pattern on the first and second beats, the and of three and the four. The emphasis, however, is on the and of three, giving the song an eccentrically lopsided feeling, which adds a great deal to its unique character.

As usual, downbeat strums on beats 1, 2 and 4 should be downstrokes, and the upbeat on the and of 3 should be an upstroke. It's important to play this very confidently, as the guitar is taking that role of the rhythm section and is responsible for securing the tempo and propelling the groove.

From bar 33 there is a melodic solo. While it's easy enough to play, there is a challenging double stop in bar 38. It is important to sustain the C note on the B string while moving the other notes (G and A) underneath; this lends an attractive piano-like flavour to the phrase.

In bars 38–39 the initial F note is held down while the other notes are sounded over it, and as they are fretted, they too are held down; by the beginning of bar 39 bar, the notes F (D string), A (G string), C (B string), and F (high E string), should be held down and left to ring for the remainder of the bar.

From bar 42 to bar 67 there is a chord/melody solo. As with the previous solo, allowing the notes to sustain and where possible holding the notes down so that one note runs into the next will create the feeling of piano played with the sustain pedal down.

Technical Exercises

In this section, you will be asked to play a selection of exercises, chosen by the examiner, from each of the groups below.

All exercises need to be played:
- From memory.
- In the keys, octaves and tempos shown.
- In either swung or straight feel, as directed by the examiner.

Note that Groups A and B need to be played to a click and any fingerings shown are suggestions only.

Group A: Scales
The tempo for this group is ♩=104 bpm.

1. E major scale

2. E blues scale

3. A♭ major scale

4. A♭ blues scale

5. C♯ natural minor scale

6. F natural minor scale

7. C♯ harmonic minor scale

8. F harmonic minor scale

9. C phrygian scale

10. Chromatic scale on E

11. Chromatic scale on A♭

Group B: Arpeggios
The tempo for this group is ♩=76 bpm.

1. E major arpeggio

2. A♭ major arpeggio

3. C♯ minor arpeggio

4. F minor arpeggio

5. C minor 7 (Cm7) arpeggio

6. C minor 11 (Cm11) arpeggio

7. C minor 13 (Cm13) arpeggio

Group C: Chord Voicings

In the exam you will be asked to play, from memory, your choice of two chord voicings from each of the following exercises, at a tempo of your choice, without the aid of a backing track or metronome. However, for practice purposes a demonstration of the chords played to a metronome click is available in the downloadable audio.

1. C dominant 9 (C9)

2. C minor 7 (Cm7)

Sight Reading

In this section you have a choice between either a sight reading test or an improvisation and interpretation test (see facing page).

The examiner will ask you which one you wish to choose before commencing. Once you have decided you cannot change your mind.

In the sight reading test, the examiner will give you a 8–16 bar melody in the key of E major or A♭ major. You will first be given 90 seconds to practise, after which the examiner will play the backing track twice. The first time is for you to practise and the second time is for you to perform the final version for the exam. For each playthrough, the backing track will begin with a one bar count-in. The tempo is ♩=60–130.

During the practice time, you will be given the choice of a metronome click throughout or a one bar count-in at the beginning.

The backing track is continuous, so once the first playthrough has finished, the count-in of the second playing will start immediately.

Please note:
- You will be required to play all notation and create appropriate parts to chord symbols.
- Time signatures will be either 4/4 or 3/4.

Sight Reading | Example 1

Please note: The test shown is an example. The examiner will give you a different version in the exam.

Sight Reading | Example 2

Please note: The test shown is an example. The examiner will give you a different version in the exam.

Improvisation & Interpretation

In the improvisation and interpretation test, the examiner will give you a 8–16 bar chord progression in the key of E major or A♭ major. You will first be given 90 seconds to practise, after which the examiner will play the backing track twice. The first time is for you to practise and the second time is for you to perform the final version for the exam. For each playthrough, the backing track will begin with a one bar count-in. The tempo is ♩=60–130.

During the practice time, you will be given the choice of a metronome click throughout or a one bar count-in at the beginning.

The backing track is continuous, so once the first playthrough has finished, the count-in of the second playing will start immediately.

You will need to improvise diatonic, single note melodies.

Please note:
- At this level, you will need to improvise as directed over the chord symbols as written.
- Time signatures will be either 4/4 or 3/4.

Improvisation & Interpretation | Example 1

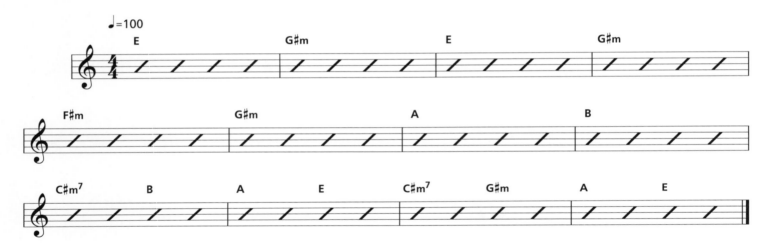

Please note: The test shown is an example. The examiner will give you a different version in the exam.

Improvisation & Interpretation | Example 2

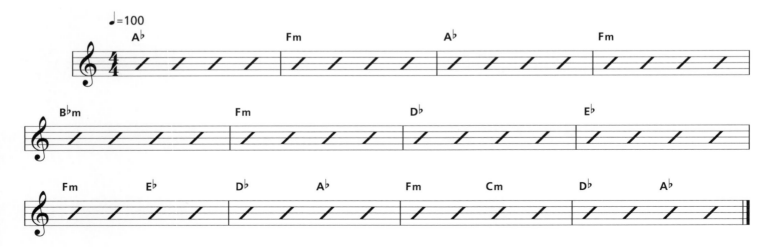

Please note: The test shown is an example. The examiner will give you a different version in the exam.

Ear Tests

In this section, there are two ear tests:
  - Melodic Recall
  - Harmonic Recall

You will find one example of each type of test printed below and you will need perform both of them in the exam.

Test 1: Melodic Recall

The examiner will play you a 2 bar diatonic melody in the key of C major with a range up to a sixth. The first note will be the root note. You will hear the test twice, each time with a one bar count-in, then you will hear a further one bar count-in after which you will need to play the melody to the click. The tempo is ♩ = 95 bpm.

It is acceptable to play over the track as it is being played as well as practicing after the second playthough. The length of time available after the second playthrough is pre-recorded on the audio track so the count-in may begin while you are still practising.

Please note: The test shown is an example. The examiner will give you a different version in the exam.

Test 2: Harmonic Recall

The examiner will play you a chord progression containing chords I, IV and V in any order or combination in the key of C major. You will hear the chord progression twice, each time with a one bar count-in. You will then hear a further one bar count in before playing back to a click. Please note, there is no requirement for the chords to be voicing-specific. The tempo is ♩ = 95 bpm.

Please note: The test shown is an example. The examiner will give you a different version in the exam.

General Musicianship Questions

The final part of your exam is the General Musicianship Questions section, which features 5 questions relating to one of your choice of the performance pieces.

1. You will be asked a question relating to the harmony from a section of one of your pieces.

2. You will be asked a question relating to the melody in a section of one of your pieces.

3. You will be asked a question relating to the rhythms used in a section of one of your pieces.

4. You will be asked a question relating to the technical requirements of one of your pieces.

5. You will be asked a question relating to the genre of one of your pieces.

Entering Rockschool Exams

Entering a Rockschool exam is easy, just go online and follow our simple six step process. All details for entering online, dates, fees, regulations and Free Choice pieces can be found at *www.rslawards.com*

- All candidates should ensure they bring their own Grade syllabus book to the exam or have their KR app ready and the full book downloaded.

- All Grade 6–8 candidates must ensure that they bring valid photo ID to their exam.

- Candidates will receive their exam results (and certificates if applicable) a maximum of 3 weeks after their exam. If nothing has been received after this time then please call +44 (0)345 460 4747 or email to *info@rslawards.com*

Marking Schemes

ELEMENT	PASS	MERIT	DISTINCTION
Performance Piece 1	12–14 out of 20	15–17 out of 20	18+ out of 20
Performance Piece 2	12–14 out of 20	15–17 out of 20	18+ out of 20
Performance Piece 3	12–14 out of 20	15–17 out of 20	18+ out of 20
Technical Exercises	9–10 out of 15	11–12 out of 15	13+ out of 15
Sight Reading or Improvisation & Interpretation	6 out of 10	7–8 out of 10	9+ out of 10
Ear Tests	6 out of 10	7–8 out of 10	9+ out of 10
General Musicianship Questions	3 out of 5	4 out of 5	5 out of 5
TOTAL MARKS	60%+	74%+	90%+

GRADE EXAMS | GRADES 6–8

ELEMENT	PASS	MERIT	DISTINCTION
Performance Piece 1	12–14 out of 20	15–17 out of 20	18+ out of 20
Performance Piece 2	12–14 out of 20	15–17 out of 20	18+ out of 20
Performance Piece 3	12–14 out of 20	15–17 out of 20	18+ out of 20
Technical Exercises	9–10 out of 15	11–12 out of 15	13+ out of 15
Quick Study Piece	6 out of 10	7–8 out of 10	9+ out of 10
Ear Tests	6 out of 10	7–8 out of 10	9+ out of 10
General Musicianship Questions	3 out of 5	4 out of 5	5 out of 5
TOTAL MARKS	60%+	74%+	90%+

PERFORMANCE CERTIFICATES | DEBUT TO GRADE 8 *

ELEMENT	PASS	MERIT	DISTINCTION
Performance Piece 1	12–14 out of 20	15–17 out of 20	18+ out of 20
Performance Piece 2	12–14 out of 20	15–17 out of 20	18+ out of 20
Performance Piece 3	12–14 out of 20	15–17 out of 20	18+ out of 20
Performance Piece 4	12–14 out of 20	15–17 out of 20	18+ out of 20
Performance Piece 5	12–14 out of 20	15–17 out of 20	18+ out of 20
TOTAL MARKS	60%+	75%+	90%+

* Note that there are no Debut Vocal exams.